SCALE SHAPES

GRADE 4

for piano

Based on the requirements for Grade 4 of
the Associated Board of the Royal Schools of Music

This book © Copyright 2002 Chester Music
Order No. CH62997
ISBN 0-7119-9025-5
Cover and template design by Phil Gambrill.
Printed in the United Kingdom.

CHESTER MUSIC
(A division of Music Sales Limited)
8/9 Frith Street, London W1D 3JB

by
FREDERICK
STOCKEN

This series of books shows scale shapes using the Stocken Method and is based on the technical exercises required by the piano grades of the Associated Board of the Royal Schools of Music. Even without the goal of an examination, the scales chosen by the Associated Board provide carefully thought-out exercises at eight levels which provide an excellent basis for daily study. It is hoped that the principles established here will soon be extended to other compilations of scales including jazz scales.

I always loved playing scales and other technical exercises as a child – and still do. However, when I came to teach the piano and organ I quickly discovered that many students, especially children, find them to be drudgery. Although the repetitive nature of the exercises is often cited as the main cause of boredom, I believe that this is not often in reality the root of the problem. The student who complains of the tedium of repetition when practising scales might well be the same person who has a fitness programme that involves plenty of repetition and which is found to be most enjoyable.

The mental block many students have with practising scales is not the repetitiveness as such, but the actual technical difficulties involved in reading musical notation and translating this into the physical shapes of the scales themselves. It is these difficulties that seem to prevent the satisfying rhythm of repetition and growing control that the student might find so rewarding when lifting weights or practising kicking a ball into a net.

The method I have invented provides a system which allows the student to concentrate exclusively on the physical shapes of the technical exercise and, in consequence, to focus on the acquisition of 'good legato, even fingers, firm tone and a musical curve' – the criteria specified by the Associated Board as 'the essential features for playing scales and arpeggios well'. In short, I have found that this method helps to make scales become fun.

The Stocken Method is not designed to be a substitute for the acquisition of the ability to read staff notation. *In fact the opposite is the case.* I have found that using this method, which so explicitly presents the physical shapes of different keys at the keyboard, actually helps fix these shapes in the student's mind so that playing from musical notation in the context of a piece or sight-reading actually becomes easier.

However idealistic a teacher may be that a student will learn a scale or technical exercise from staff notation, experience shows that the simplest method of introducing a new scale or other technical exercise is often for the teacher physically to play the exercise demonstrating the new shape for the student to copy. The Stocken Method not only removes this stage of teaching, saving valuable time during lessons, but also gives the student a system for the exercise that he or she will be confident of being able to re-read when the teacher has gone.

At the earlier stages of learning, a simple scale may involve ledger lines or other symbols that are far in advance of the pieces a student may be playing. This is the case right from the beginning when the introduction of a C major scale of two octaves for instance will use a great many more notes in different octaves than the student will have encountered in staff notation.

Many students at much higher levels continue to find key signatures and other aspects of staff notation confusing and find the simplicity of this method to be of great help.

In fact one of the revolutionary aspects of the Stocken Method is that the complications of staff notation are no longer linked to the often quite different physical complications of actually playing a given scale. This means that scales which have, until now, seemed more difficult than others, mainly because of the complexity of their representation using staff notation, are now, using this method, suddenly found to be easier. The implication of this for the order in which scales have traditionally been introduced to the student is far-reaching.

Frederick Stocken.

The Associated Board of the Royal Schools of Music list the following requirements for Grade 4 in its piano syllabus:

SCALES, ARPEGGIOS AND BROKEN CHORDS:
from memory.

SCALES:
major and minor (melodic *or* harmonic at candidate's choice):
(i) in similar motion with hands together one octave apart, **up and down**, hands separately and together, in the following keys:

> B, B♭, E♭, A♭, D♭ majors (two octaves)
> C♯, G♯, C, F minors (two octaves)

(ii) in contrary motion with both hands beginning and ending on the key-note (unison), in the keys of F and B♭ majors, and D and G *harmonic* minors (two octaves).

CHROMATIC SCALES:
in similar motion with hands together one octave apart, and with each hand separately, beginning on any black key named by the examiner (two octaves), **up and down.**

ARPEGGIOS:
(i) the common chords of E, B and F majors, in root position only, in similar motion with hands together one octave apart, and with each hand separately (two octaves), **up and down.**
(ii) the common chords of E♭, A♭ and D♭ majors, and C♯, G♯, C and F minors, in root position only, with each hand separately (two octaves), **up and down.**

BROKEN CHORDS:
formed from the chords of B♭ major and G minor, with each hand separately, according to *both* the following patterns:

Pattern 1

Pattern 2 **and:**

(L.H. fingering and starting notes as appropriate)

Contents

B MAJOR SCALE

Hands separately and together an octave apart in similar motion: 2 Octaves.

♩ = 52 *(minimum speed recommended by the ABRSM)*

B♭ MAJOR SCALE

Hands separately and together an octave apart in similar motion: 2 Octaves.

*N.B. The scales (including contrary motion and chromatic) are written without a time signature
in groups of four quavers with the final note as a crotchet.*

E♭ MAJOR SCALE

Hands separately and together an octave apart in similar motion: 2 Octaves.

A♭ MAJOR SCALE

Hands separately and together an octave apart in similar motion: 2 Octaves.

Db MAJOR SCALE
(ENHARMONIC C#)

Hands separately and together an octave apart in similar motion: 2 Octaves.

Minor Scales (melodic or harmonic at candidate's choice)

C# MINOR MELODIC SCALE

Hands separately and together an octave apart in similar motion: 2 Octaves.

G# MINOR MELODIC SCALE
(ENHARMONIC A♭)

Hands separately and together an octave apart in similar motion: 2 Octaves.

C MINOR MELODIC SCALE

Hands separately and together an octave apart in similar motion: 2 Octaves.

F MINOR MELODIC SCALE

Hands separately and together an octave apart in similar motion: 2 Octaves.

C♯ MINOR HARMONIC SCALE

Hands separately and together an octave apart in similar motion: 2 Octaves.

G♯ MINOR HARMONIC SCALE (ENHARMONIC A♭)

Hands separately and together an octave apart in similar motion: 2 Octaves.

C MINOR HARMONIC SCALE

Hands separately and together an octave apart in similar motion: 2 Octaves.

F MINOR HARMONIC SCALE

Hands separately and together an octave apart in similar motion: 2 Octaves.

F MAJOR CONTRARY MOTION

Hands together beginning and ending on the key-note (unison): 2 Octaves.
Notes played together with both hands are shown using the same geometric shape.

♩ = 52 *(minimum speed recommended by the ABRSM)*

B♭ MAJOR CONTRARY MOTION

Hands together beginning and ending on the key-note (unison): 2 Octaves.
Notes played together with both hands are shown using the same geometric shape.

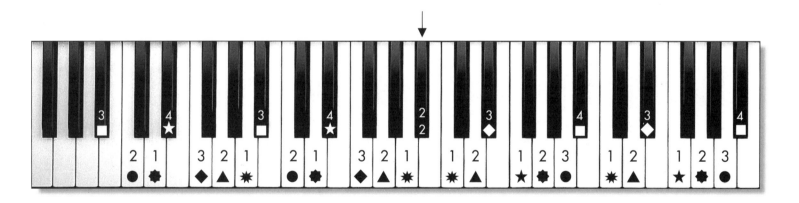

D MINOR CONTRARY MOTION

Hands together beginning and ending on the key-note (unison): 2 Octaves.
Notes played together with both hands are shown using the same geometric shape.

G MINOR CONTRARY MOTION

Hands together beginning and ending on the key-note (unison): 2 Octaves.
Notes played together with both hands are shown using the same geometric shape.

CHROMATIC SCALE BEGINNING ON F♯/G♭

Hands separately and together an octave apart in similar motion: 2 Octaves.

♩= 52 *(minimum speed recommended by the ABRSM)*

CHROMATIC SCALE BEGINNING ON G♯/A♭

Hands separately and together an octave apart in similar motion: 2 Octaves.

CHROMATIC SCALE BEGINNING ON B♭/A♯

Hands separately and together an octave apart in similar motion: 2 Octaves.

CHROMATIC SCALE BEGINNING ON C♯/D♭

Hands separately and together an octave apart in similar motion: 2 Octaves.

CHROMATIC SCALE BEGINNING ON E♭/D♯

Hands separately and together an octave apart in similar motion: 2 Octaves.

E MAJOR ARPEGGIO

*Hands separately **and** together an octave apart: 2 Octaves.*

♩ = 76 *(minimum speed recommended by the ABRSM)*

★ *Alternative 4*

B MAJOR ARPEGGIO

*Hands separately **and** together an octave apart: 2 Octaves.*

★ *Alternative 4*

N.B. The arpeggios are written without a time signature in groups of four quavers with the final note as a crotchet.

F MAJOR ARPEGGIO

*Hands separately **and** together an octave apart: 2 Octaves.*

★ *Alternative 3*

E♭ MAJOR ARPEGGIO

*Hands separately **only** an octave apart: 2 Octaves.*

★ *Alternative 3*

Arpeggios (hands separately only)

A♭ MAJOR ARPEGGIO

*Hands separately **only** an octave apart: 2 Octaves.*

* Alternative 3

D♭ MAJOR ARPEGGIO (ENHARMONIC C♯)

*Hands separately **only** an octave apart: 2 Octaves.*

C♯ MINOR ARPEGGIO

*Hands separately **only** an octave apart: 2 Octaves.*

★ *Alternative 3*

G♯ MINOR ARPEGGIO (ENHARMONIC A♭)

*Hands separately **only** an octave apart: 2 Octaves.*

★ *Alternative 3*

Arpeggios (hands separately only)

C MINOR ARPEGGIO

*Hands separately **only** an octave apart: 2 Octaves.*

* Alternative 3

F MINOR ARPEGGIO

*Hands separately **only** an octave apart: 2 Octaves.*

* Alternative 3

B♭ MAJOR BROKEN CHORD

Hands separately. The patterns for broken chords are:

Left Hand

Right Hand

G MINOR BROKEN CHORD

Hands separately. The patterns for broken chords are:

Left Hand

Right Hand

★ *Alternative 3 (pattern 1 only)*